The Birthday Present

by Mavis Smith

SCHOLASTIC INC.

New York   Toronto   London   Auckland   Sydney

Copyright © 1994 by Scholastic Inc.
All rights reserved. Published by Scholastic Inc.
Printed in the U.S.A.
ISBN 0-590-27524-0
ISBN 0-590-29344-3 (meets NASTA specifications)

2 3 4 5 6 7 8 9 10   09   01 00 99 98 97 96 95 94

SHIRTS

13